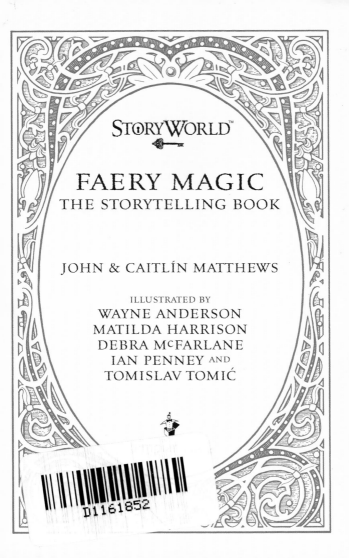

STORYWORLD

FAERY MAGIC
THE STORYTELLING BOOK

JOHN & CAITLÍN MATTHEWS

ILLUSTRATED BY
WAYNE ANDERSON
MATILDA HARRISON
DEBRA McFARLANE
IAN PENNEY AND
TOMISLAV TOMIĆ

> "And if thou keep my just command,
> One day thou shalt see Fairy Land."
> From 'Robin Goodfellow', Anonymous,
> 17th century

ONCE UPON A TIME... when people still lived in caves and would sit around the fire every night, storytellers used their magic to keep the vast and silent darkness at bay. Their tales hopped off the tongue and into the ear, taking root in the imaginations of their listeners. There, each tale grew wide and tall, put flesh on its bones, and then walked about in the world.

This Faery Magic pack is part of the StoryWorld series, a wonderful toolkit to inspire storytellers. In this pack you will discover some of the people, places, creatures and special objects that can be found in the ever-living world of the faeries. By taking just a few cards and using their pictures, titles or questions as inspiration, even those who are new to storytelling will be able to create their own tales.

Faeries such as THE FAERY GODMOTHER often help humans, becoming an essential part of what we call 'fairy tales', which are told all over the world. Faeries are a race of beings who live beside us, though we rarely see them. Unlike human beings who live through time, faeries live outside of time. But some humans have visited them, like Tam Lin, who met THE FAERY QUEEN and lived in FAERYLAND for seven human years. (His story became a Scottish folk tale.) You can meet faeries too, if you look and listen carefully.

PICTURE YOUR STORY

Begin by taking out all the Faery Magic cards and looking at them. Which ones seem to jump into your hands right away and demand to have their stories told? Lay these cards in front of you and look at their pictures – pictures tell their own stories, so look carefully at each card – what ideas for tales are they whispering to you? Every time you place two cards side by side, a different tale will spring to your mind.

The picture on each card also contains a hidden visual link to another card in your Faery Magic pack. Take out a few cards now and see if you can spot one. Every card is connected to another in the pack, creating a circle of hidden links. Try playing a game where you arrange all of your cards in the order of their hidden links, then use that order to tell a story. (If you need help spotting the links, go to page 23 for the full list.)

FREE YOUR IMAGINATION

There are a huge number of ways in which the cards can be used to spark story ideas. The suggestions we give you here are just a starting place – using your imagination and inventiveness, you will find a limitless number of new ways to create your stories. The names and pictures of four or five cards can inspire a whole adventure. Try randomly picking a few cards to see where you can take those characters. Look at the questions on each card – they might take your tale in an unexpected direction.

There is no right or wrong way to use the StoryWorld Cards. Free yourself from that idea and you will discover millions of untold stories. There are more StoryWorld Cards to collect, available in separate packs with themes such as quests, sea adventures and animals.

TELL THE TALE

There are many ways to tell a story: you can tell it out loud to someone else, write it down in pictures or words, or you can act it out with a group of friends – each of you can be a character, or you can take turns telling different parts of the story.

The great thing about telling a tale with the StoryWorld Cards is that you can create a new story every time. Try choosing your favourite cards to make a story or, if you like a challenge, pick some cards at random and see what kind of tale unfolds!

Remember, you are the storyteller and you have the power to bring to life the millions of untold tales that lie within your imagination. If you want to include an interesting character, place or object that isn't in your StoryWorld Cards, why not create a card of your own? Take a piece of blank cardboard, lay a StoryWorld Card on top of it and draw around it. Cut out the new blank card, draw or stick a picture on it, give it a title and some questions, then add your new StoryWorld Card to your pack.

STORYTELLING GAMES

You can play games with your StoryWorld Cards, alone or with friends, to discover new tales. With a friend, try taking a card each and pretending to be that card. For example, what happens if THE GREEN CHILDREN meet THE GUARDIAN OF THE WAYS? What does it feel like to be those characters and what do they say to each other? If you get stuck, try asking the questions on the back of the cards. Pick another card to end your story.

If you are alone, or on a long journey, choose three cards to be the beginning, middle and end of your story. For a special game to play with your Faery Magic cards, go to page 22.

KEEP ASKING QUESTIONS

Questions are the key to great storytelling. If your story gets stuck, ask questions about the story, place or object on the StoryWorld Card. Where are they travelling to and what will happen next? Who might be watching them? If you ask enough questions, you'll find there is a story to be told about everyone and everything.

Once you are familiar with your Faery Magic cards, read the yellow section of this book to discover more ideas about each card in the pack. Use the Keywords in your storytelling.

⬥ A NOTE FOR THOSE WORKING WITH ⬥
YOUNG STORYTELLERS

StoryWorld is first and foremost intended to be inspiring and exciting, but this also makes it a very useful educational tool.

Storytelling is a vital way to stimulate the imagination and is a cornerstone in the development of literacy and communication skills like listening, speaking, reading and writing. It also builds vocabulary and the understanding of key concepts such as comprehension and sequencing (deciding the correct order of things) – vital knowledge for storytellers of all ages.

Whether a child is pre-literate, learning to read or already a confident reader, he or she can benefit from playing with different aspects of the cards. If you are using the StoryWorld Cards with a child or a group of children, you will discover new ways to stimulate their imaginations through sharing the magic of storytelling.

Cards used in this story:
THE FAERY SHIELD, THE THREE WISHES, THE MERRY
SHOEMAKER, THE HILL OF PLAYING, THE FAERY GODMOTHER

One day while Jamie was playing, he found a shield on
the ground. Suddenly a mist came down and he had to
feel his way until it cleared. Before him was a tree, with
a nest in its low branches. In the nest were three fat eggs,
and on the nest sat a strange bird which sang, "Wishes
three I grant to thee."

Jamie thought quickly, "I wish for a good pair of shoes."

"Granted," said the bird.

One of the eggs cracked open and out jumped a pair
of magic shoes that immediately started to run away.

"I wish for friends who will play with me and come
on adventures," said Jamie hastily, hoping he would be
able to catch the magic shoes.

"Wish granted," said the bird.

Another egg cracked open and the sound of laughter
and playing drifted down to Jamie. Now, Jamie had heard
tales about faeries and knew he had to choose his last
wish carefully – he did not want to waste such good luck.

"Lastly, I wish for a faery godmother who will always
help me to get out of trouble," he said.

"She shall be yours," said the bird.

The last egg cracked open, and out of it rose a magic
wand which immediately flew over Jamie's head. The bird
said to Jamie, "Run quickly and catch your wishes, boy!"

Jamie ran after the shoes first. They led him past the
Merry Shoemaker, who was stitching a pair of green boots.

"Sir, please help me – how can I stop those shoes from running away?" asked Jamie.

"Shout, 'You were made for me!', and when they stop, put them on as quickly as you can," said the Shoemaker.

"You were made for me!" shouted Jamie. The shoes stopped in the middle of the path and Jamie put them on.

With the magic shoes on his feet, Jamie could run much faster. He followed the sound of laughter and playing that drifted on the wind, until he came to a high hill. The hill was covered in children, playing games, running races and telling stories. A beautiful girl with a crown of flowers smiled when she saw Jamie and said to him, "Come and join us!"

She took Jamie's hand and he joined their games – he ran races, climbed trees, and won the tug-of-war. They played all day. As the sun set over the hill, Jamie noticed that the flowers on the hill were as tall as trees.

"I have become very small," he said, beginning to feel frightened – he would never get home on these tiny legs! But then Jamie remembered he still had one last wish.

He ran after the magic wand, waggling in the air, and saw it jump into the hand of the Faery Godmother.

"Faery Godmother," panted Jamie, "I'm too small to get home. Please, I need your help!"

The Faery Godmother waved her wand, saying:

"Wishes three you chose today:
Magic shoes led you to play.
You shrank small, now grown once more.
Be as happy as before!"

Jamie opened his eyes – he was back to his normal size, standing on the path that led home. He felt very glad that he'd wished for a faery godmother.

THE FAERY KING

KEYWORDS: protection, guidance, strength.

I AM the ruler of all the Lands of Faery. When you come into my realm you must tread carefully, speak wisely and behave as if everything you see and meet is your friend. If I hear that you have brought evil into my realm, you will regret it, for my hounds will chase you far away from here. But fear not! If you come with an open mind and a warm heart, you are welcome. My hounds will show you the secret paths through the forests and you will grow strong in my service.

THE FAERY QUEEN

KEYWORDS: wisdom, hope, compassion, tenderness.

I AM the queen who can grant wishes. The Land of Faery is my delight and pleasure. Those who are pure of heart will easily find me, for their goodness makes a bridge between us. I have powers to open doors for those who have lost hope. I offer my magical draft to all who want to share my wisdom: drink from my shell if you so desire. But beware – you will never be the same again, for you will see things as I do. I am the heart of Faeryland and the answer to your tangled problems. If you call out to me, my messengers will find you.

THE FAERY GODMOTHER

KEYWORDS: comfort, help, magical protection.

I AM the one who will give protection when parents cannot. Be assured that everyone has their own faery godmother, though not everyone knows how to contact her. When you are feeling sad and sorry, I bring comfort and listen to your side of the story. From my bottomless bag I can draw out whatever you need. My wand directs help to you, though it will not take away those problems that you must solve for yourself. While you are growing, I will always be near you, ready to help and listen.

THE MERRY SHOEMAKER

KEYWORDS: making and mending, destiny, luck.

I MAKE shoes that lead the wearer down paths never dreamed of. When you are asleep at night, I take the measure of your feet and return to my secret workshop. A few mornings later, you will wake up to find a pair of shoes beside your bed. If you are a curious child, I will make you a pair of shoes that will lead you into mischief, for that is what you enjoy best. If you are seeking adventure, I will make special shoes that will lead you along unknown ways to seek treasure or find new friends.

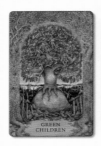 

THE GREEN CHILDREN

KEYWORDS: friends, travellers, old stories, loss.

WE CAN be guides in the faery realms, if we are fed well. We walked into the Land of Faery long ago and forgot all about the human world. We were watching our flock of sheep when we heard the sweet sound of a bell chiming. We followed it and came to this place. That must have been long ago, because we don't remember our old homes. Please give us some green food to eat – that's what we like best, as we can't eat human food yet. If we like you, we will tell you stories about the places we've seen or lead you back into the Land of Faery.

FAERYLAND

KEYWORDS: delight, mystery, return.

I AM the land that all children dream of. Do you dare to step within? The best times to find your way inside are when dawn or twilight send their long light across the land. Then, if you stand between two trees or pass over a stream, you may find a secret entrance. Many humans have visited me and found the deep joy of living outside of time. Some grow younger, others never age. Those who live in the Faeryland find peace and joy, and never want to leave. I invite you to visit me and seek out what your heart desires.

THE VALLEY BEYOND TIME

KEYWORDS: peace, plenty, ancestors, joy.

I AM the land that is always young, where time no longer runs. In my land live people from ancient times, times so old you have forgotten them. Time has stopped for my people, so they live inside their own time forever. They are the ever-living neighbours of the faeries, who live outside of time. When you need special help that no one else can give, my people will come. If you notice them, you'll wonder why they are wearing such old-fashioned clothes. But you are not ready to join them, so they will just give you help and then wish you well.

THE THREE WISHES

KEYWORDS: wishes, desires, thoughtfulness.

WE ARE the wishes you must use with care. But stop! Don't speak your wishes yet. Think about what you want most of all and, if you had it, how would it change things for you and for those who live around you? The boy who wished to live forever, but forgets to ask for eternal health as well might regret his choice when his body is frail and old. So make your wish with care. Once you speak your wishes aloud, we cannot stop them from coming true. So consider, what would make the world a happier place for others, not just for yourself?

THE HEALING APPLE

KEYWORDS: healing, energy, restoration.

I AM the apple that can cure all sickness. I grow in the orchards of the Valley of Promise, deep within Faeryland, where there is no sickness or death. All the strength of the faeries lies within me. If someone finds me and takes me back to the human world, just one bite from me will restore them to full health. However many bites you take, I will never be used up. If you lack health, then seek me and I will bring you energy such as you have never felt before.

THE HOMEWARD PATH

KEYWORDS: homecoming, familiar, welcome.

I AM the path that leads to home. When you set foot upon me, you may feel both sad and glad – sad that you are leaving the Land of Faery behind, and glad that you can see the way home. I lead your feet from unknown places right to your front door. Every tree and bush will stretch out its boughs to welcome you home, every bird will sing at your return. Your pets can feel you coming – your dog will bark and your cat will jump upon the windowsill to greet you. I can take you to the end of your adventure, or to the beginning of a new one.

THE SPELL OF DANCING

KEYWORDS: unending, invisible, whirl.

I AM the spell that will make you dance until you drop. It begins with an itching in your toes, then a lifting of your knees and, before you know it, you are dancing. I dance the farmer from behind his plough, the boy from his game and the girl from her swing. The world whirls around you as you dance to an invisible music and rhythm that no one else can feel, until you faint from exhaustion. The only cure is to speak a blessing or find a charm, if only you could stand still long enough!

THE MIDNIGHT MUSHROOMS

KEYWORDS: growing, shrinking, nocturnal power.

WE MAKE the houses of the smallest faery folk. We grow while you are asleep, pushing up from under the ground when no one is watching and disappearing if you glance away. We have the gift of making things smaller or larger: nibble a piece of us and you can shrink as small as a beetle or as large as the old oak tree. Every mushroom spoor from the underside of our roofs is a seed that can create a hundred more faery cities. Look beneath your feet and you might see us.

THE GREEN STONE

KEYWORDS: promises, neighbours, gratitude.

I AM the boundary stone between the human and faery worlds. I have been here since ancient times when your ancestors knew the faeries as their neighbours. Offerings of milk and cream were brought to them here. I am the place where agreements and promises are made between these two worlds. If you want to call the faeries, pour a bowl of water upon me. This will change the weather – the wind will rise, blowing the leaves off the trees, or a thunder storm will make the earth shake. Then the faeries will come to witness your promise.

THE FAERY DART

KEYWORDS: revenge, attack, offence, justice.

I AM the dart that finds the wrongdoer. I am coming right towards you and will strike unless you have a shield. What have you done to provoke this attack, you ask? I was shot by the faery archer who creates strife. Long ago, a thoughtless human offended him and now he shoots his darts into the air, aiming at those who have wronged the faeries. Whoever is struck by me will sicken fast or change their shape so that even their own family will no longer recognise them. Humans call this "being elf-shot". There is one sure cure, but only the Faery King or Queen can tell you that.

THE FAERY CHARM

KEYWORDS: strength, invisibility, illumination.

I AM the charm that will make you strong. If anyone has cursed you or hurt you, then I will make you whole again. Anyone who finds this charm and wears it will hold a lantern of light against the darkness. I am not magic as you know it; mine is not the gift of deception. Those who wish you harm will instinctively know that you are stronger than they. They will feel the power of the charm. Enemies will leave you alone, and spies and sneaks will not see you pass beneath their very noses. You will come and go safely under my protection.

THE FAERY SHIELD

KEYWORDS: warmth, courage, magical defence.

I AM the shield that protects against stealthy attacks. I am made of the alder tree which stands with its roots in the water. I can send back rain and bad weather to clear the way before you, keeping you warm and dry. I burst into red, glorious flame in every battle. Whenever a dart or spear is thrown against me, I send it back to the thrower. Whenever danger threatens, make sure that you pick me up and place me in front of your heart as a breastplate. I will fight for you in every struggle.

THE FAERY HOST
KEYWORDS: keeping peace, checking boundaries.

WE ARE the unstoppable gathering of the faeries. Do we scare you? If ever you see us coming, run away and hide or you will be swept along with us. It isn't often you will see us together like this. Twice each year, at May Eve and Hallowe'en we assemble and march through our realm and around our borders. No one can stop our passing. We also gather like this to go into battle, with our swords, our shields, our terrible eyes and our cries that pierce the night. We are the keepers of peace, but do not expect us to be gentle towards wrongdoers.

THE BROWNIE
KEYWORDS: tidiness, sharing, disorder.

I WILL look after your house, if you treat me kindly. I live in your house, but you won't see me. If you leave a saucer of milk and a slice of bread near the fire, I will look after your house, tidying up and cleaning. But if you ignore me, then I will drop your clean washing in the muddy yard and knock over your furniture. I don't appear to humans often, because I do my tasks when they're asleep. If you move house, then I will move with you because I am like a member of the family. But don't offer me a gift of clothing because then we will have to leave you.

THE FAERY MESSENGER

KEYWORDS: messages, stealth, remembrance.

I AM the messenger between the faery and human worlds. I take messages for the Faery King and Queen. Those who go about their business don't notice me because I am small and easily overlooked. I can easily pass between the worlds, but not everyone can hear my messages. Humans forget that something small can be more important than something very large. If you stop what you are doing and listen hard, you will be able to hear the message that is meant for you. Every message starts with the same words: "Only remember..."

THE CHANGELING

KEYWORDS: frustration, annoyance, naughtiness.

I AM the ones that the faeries left, when they took the human baby. I don't like it here – time passes too slowly for a changeling. I'm always hungry and the mother and father leave me alone too much, no matter how much I cry. I'm here to learn as much about humans as I can, but it's sometimes too easy to tease my human family. I pull out the plugs and make the lights go out. I pour milk over the floor and I break the mother's best vase. When she looks at me, I smile sweetly to tell her that it definitely wasn't me!

THE FIDDLER

KEYWORDS: music, delight, faithfulness.

I AM one who makes music at the crossroads. I play the sweet tunes that make you dance and sing. I learnt some of them from the faeries and I have many a tale to tell about them. I've noticed that if you keep true to the faery music, no one will ever trap or deceive you. I play in all weathers for the sake of the tune that flows through me like a river – I heard it playing when I was a young boy and I still follow it now. What is the tune that plays through you? Just follow your tune and see where it leads you.

THE HILL OF PLAYING

KEYWORDS: play, fun, games, togetherness.

I AM the hill where faeries come to play their games. The people who live below know that this is the faeries' special place and so they stay away, but if children climb the hill, they will find many games they can join in with. Lie down on me when you are bored or lonely and I will show you new ways to play. I will tell you stories and sing you songs that you'll be able to share with others. Come and join us as we play!

THE WOODS SO WILD

KEYWORDS: dangers, wonders, forgotten secrets.

I AM the home of many wonders and dangers. Enter me if you dare. No woodsman has come here with an axe, for I grew before humans walked the Earth. Only someone very determined would be able to come here, or someone very small who could creep between my thick branches. There are paths within me, if you can find them, but the sun rarely penetrates far into my depths. You may find what you seek within me, but tread carefully, or my watchmen will lead you astray in my ancient, winding roots.

THE FAERY DEER

KEYWORDS: luck, speed, finding, blessing.

I AM the deer who can bless you with good fortune. Can you see me in the brightness of the glade? Then I can lead you to the blessed Land of Faery, to the adventures that you have yearned for. Follow me quickly, because I am fleet of foot. I leave no footprint for you to find. I know the secret ways between the worlds and can run along them in the twinkling of an eye. I dart like quicksilver so you must not lose sight of me. I can get to the heart of all that you love and find those things you thought were lost.

THE FAERY RING

KEYWORDS: celebration, company, gladness, renewal.

I AM the ring where the faeries dance. Legend has it that my circle was made from people who were turned to stone and it is nearly right. Long ago, even the humans knew that I was the faery's dancing ring, so they set up my stones to honour the faeries and to dance themselves. Now this is where the faeries hold their festivities; every season, they gather here to dance hand in hand, to help spring turn to summer, summer to autumn, autumn to winter and winter back to spring again. Their dancing gladdens the earth and makes it want to change.

THE GUARDIAN OF THE WAYS

KEYWORDS: safeguard, guidance, obstacles.

I AM the guardian who patrols the paths into Faeryland. I make sure that no one strays in who shouldn't and that those who need to go there can find their way. I am a guard and a companion on the road. If you are lost and need a guide, I will send an animal to show the way: it might be a blackbird who flies and sings alongside you or a fox who barks to lead you on. But if someone comes to bring mischief, I will close the ways with brambles that will grow across the paths at my command.

THE TANGLE-GATE

KEYWORDS: barrier, protection, deflecting harm.

I AM the gate that can keep out all danger. Some people never imagine what lies beyond the paths they know and rush in without thinking. I also guard you in other ways. Your ancestors set me up here so that I would tangle all ill will that might come towards your home. By the time any spitefulness has traced its way around my twisting turns, it becomes too tired and confused to do any harm. Do not take me down, for I am here to keep you safe. Just dust my pathways from time to time and I will serve you well.

THE FAERY PATH

KEYWORDS: desire, truth, daring, dream-stories.

I AM the magical path into Faeryland. Many wish they could find the way here, but I am a secret path and even if they discover me, not everyone is brave enough to follow me all the way. Some say I lead from the deepest part of your heart and that I show myself in dreams. This is certainly my straightest path. If someone intends to follow me in order to do malicious things, they will find themselves lost as my pathway twists and turns, taking them far from where they want to go. Look for the clues that are hidden along my way and listen for the singing of the birds.

THE TRAVELLING FAERY GAME

The Travelling Faery Game can be played by yourself or in a group, with each person taking a turn to tell one part of the story.

To play, split your pack into three piles – your star pile, your travelling pile and your action pile. Without looking, pick a card from the star pile – that will be the creature, object or place that will star in your story, having travelled to our world from the faery realms.

Once you have chosen the card, use it to begin your story, (for example, "This is THE FAERY MESSENGER,") adding any details about them that your imagination suggests. (You can do all of this out loud – more fun in a group – or you can write the whole story down.)

Next, pick a card from the travelling pile and use that creature, object or place to explain how or why your star card has come to our world.

To continue your story, pick a card from the action pile – this creature, object or place will be involved in what happens to your star card in the human world. To end your story, pick a final card from the travelling pile to take your tale to its end.

If you enjoy this game, why not try it again, but this time have a star card that comes from the human world and travels to the faery realms!

❦ THE HIDDEN LINKS ❦

THE FAERY KING	— THE FAERY SHIELD
THE FAERY QUEEN	— THE HEALING APPLE
THE FAERY GODMOTHER	— THE FAERY DEER
THE MERRY SHOEMAKER	— THE FAERY PATH
THE GREEN CHILDREN	— THE WOODS SO WILD
FAERYLAND	— THE CHANGELING
THE VALLEY BEYOND TIME	— THE FAERY RING
THE THREE WISHES	— THE FAERY QUEEN
THE HEALING APPLE	— THE GREEN CHILDREN
THE HOMEWARD PATH	— THE FAERY MESSENGER
THE SPELL OF DANCING	— THE MERRY SHOEMAKER
THE MIDNIGHT MUSHROOMS	— THE FAERY GODMOTHER
THE GREEN STONE	— THE BROWNIE
THE FAERY DART	— THE HILL OF PLAYING
THE FAERY CHARM	— THE MIDNIGHT MUSHROOMS
THE FAERY SHIELD	— THE HOMEWARD PATH
THE FAERY HOST	— THE THREE WISHES
THE BROWNIE	— THE GUARDIAN OF THE WAYS
THE FAERY MESSENGER	— THE VALLEY BEYOND TIME
THE CHANGELING	— THE TANGLE-GATE
THE FIDDLER	— FAERYLAND
THE HILL OF PLAYING	— THE FAERY DART
THE WOODS SO WILD	— THE FAERY CHARM
THE FAERY DEER	— THE FIDDLER
THE FAERY RING	— THE SPELL OF DANCING
THE GUARDIAN OF THE WAYS	— THE FAERY KING
THE TANGLE-GATE	— THE GREEN STONE
THE FAERY PATH	— THE FAERY HOST

To Jane May, with gratitude for her guardianship
of the ways between – C.M. & J.M.

A TEMPLAR BOOK

First published in the UK in 2009 by Templar Publishing,
an imprint of The Templar Company Limited,
The Granary, North Street, Dorking, Surrey, RH4 1DN, UK
www.templarco.co.uk

ISBN 978-1-84011-734-9

Designed by Mike Jolley
Edited by Libby Hamilton

Manufactured in China

— THE —
FAERY PATH

Illustrated by MATILDA HARRISON

STORYWORLD

— THE —

FAERY PATH

I AM THE MAGICAL PATH
INTO FAERYLAND.

Who might help you to
find me?

If a traveller takes one of my
pebbles, what will happen?

What do the plants that
line my path whisper?

— THE —

HEALING
APPLE

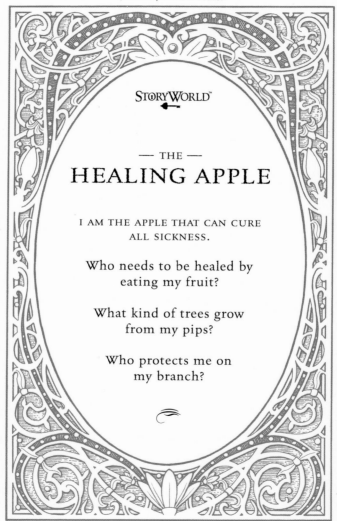

STORYWORLD™

— THE —
HEALING APPLE

I AM THE APPLE THAT CAN CURE
ALL SICKNESS.

Who needs to be healed by
eating my fruit?

What kind of trees grow
from my pips?

Who protects me on
my branch?

— THE —
HOMEWARD
PATH

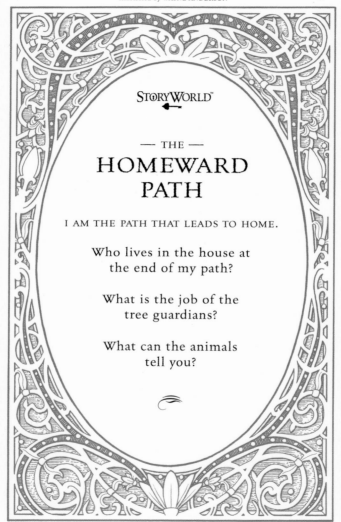

STORYWORLD™

— THE —

HOMEWARD PATH

I AM THE PATH THAT LEADS TO HOME.

Who lives in the house at
the end of my path?

What is the job of the
tree guardians?

What can the animals
tell you?

— THE —
TANGLE-
GATE

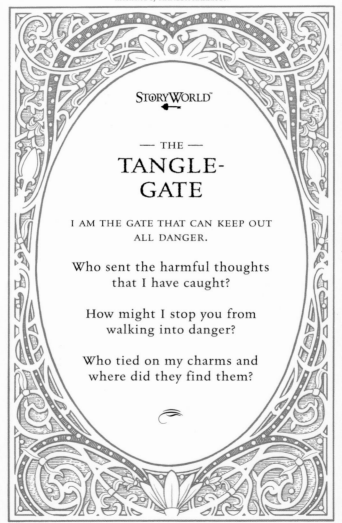

StoryWorld™

— THE —

TANGLE-GATE

I AM THE GATE THAT CAN KEEP OUT
ALL DANGER.

Who sent the harmful thoughts
that I have caught?

How might I stop you from
walking into danger?

Who tied on my charms and
where did they find them?

— THE —

VALLEY
BEYOND TIME

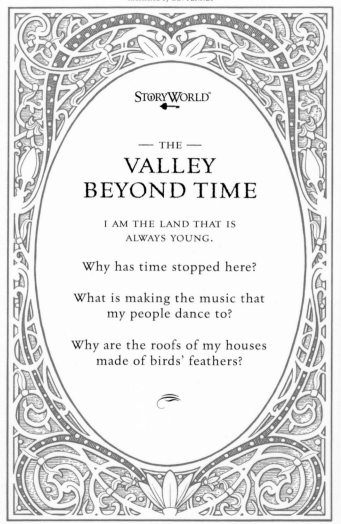

STORYWORLD™

— THE —

VALLEY BEYOND TIME

I AM THE LAND THAT IS
ALWAYS YOUNG.

Why has time stopped here?

What is making the music that
my people dance to?

Why are the roofs of my houses
made of birds' feathers?

— THE —
FAERY SHIELD

Illustrated by DEBRA MCFARLANE

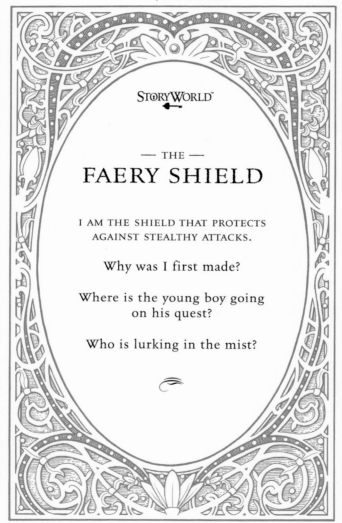

STORYWORLD™

— THE —
FAERY SHIELD

I AM THE SHIELD THAT PROTECTS
AGAINST STEALTHY ATTACKS.

Why was I first made?

Where is the young boy going
on his quest?

Who is lurking in the mist?

— THE —
FAERY HOST

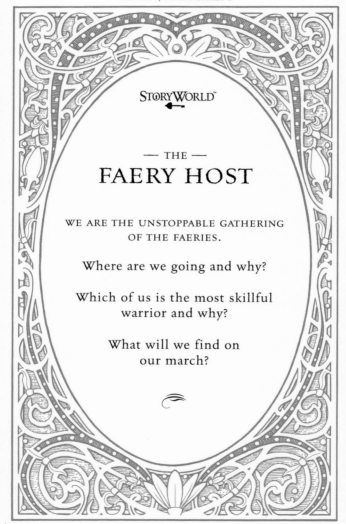

STORYWORLD™

— THE —
FAERY HOST

WE ARE THE UNSTOPPABLE GATHERING
OF THE FAERIES.

Where are we going and why?

Which of us is the most skillful
warrior and why?

What will we find on
our march?

— THE —
BROWNIE

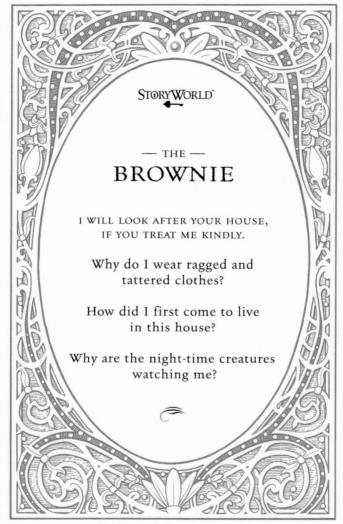

STORYWORLD™

— THE —
BROWNIE

I WILL LOOK AFTER YOUR HOUSE,
IF YOU TREAT ME KINDLY.

Why do I wear ragged and
tattered clothes?

How did I first come to live
in this house?

Why are the night-time creatures
watching me?

— THE —
FAERY
MESSENGER

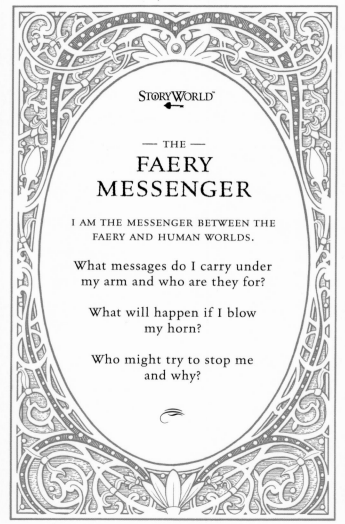

STORYWORLD™

— THE —
FAERY MESSENGER

I AM THE MESSENGER BETWEEN THE
FAERY AND HUMAN WORLDS.

What messages do I carry under
my arm and who are they for?

What will happen if I blow
my horn?

Who might try to stop me
and why?

— THE —
CHANGELING

Illustrated by DEBRA MCFARLANE

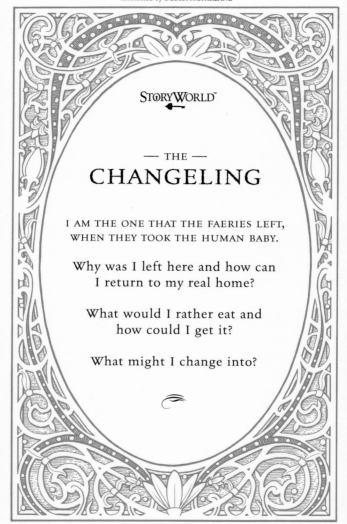

STORYWORLD™

— THE —
CHANGELING

I AM THE ONE THAT THE FAERIES LEFT,
WHEN THEY TOOK THE HUMAN BABY.

Why was I left here and how can
I return to my real home?

What would I rather eat and
how could I get it?

What might I change into?

— THE —
FIDDLER

Illustrated by DEBRA MCFARLANE

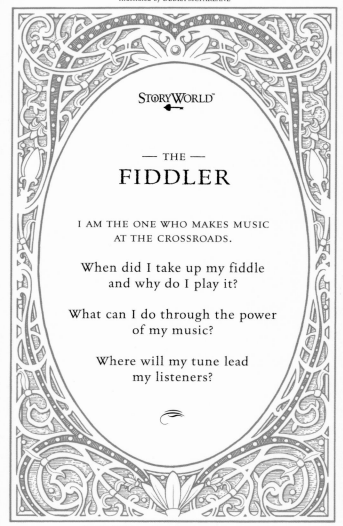

STORYWORLD™

— THE —
FIDDLER

I AM THE ONE WHO MAKES MUSIC
AT THE CROSSROADS.

When did I take up my fiddle
and why do I play it?

What can I do through the power
of my music?

Where will my tune lead
my listeners?

THE

WOODS
SO WILD

Illustrated by MATILDA HARRISON

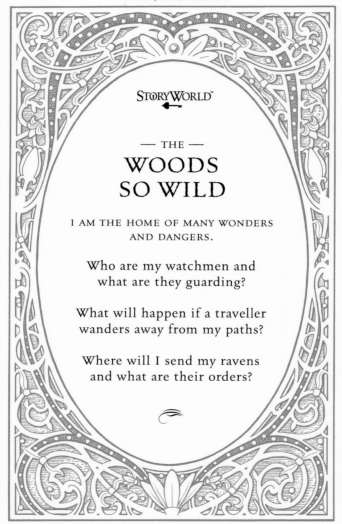

StoryWorld™

— THE —

WOODS SO WILD

I AM THE HOME OF MANY WONDERS
AND DANGERS.

Who are my watchmen and
what are they guarding?

What will happen if a traveller
wanders away from my paths?

Where will I send my ravens
and what are their orders?

THE —

FAERY
DEER

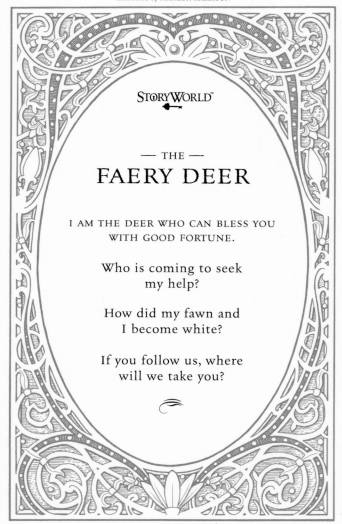

STORY**W**ORLD™

— THE —

FAERY DEER

I AM THE DEER WHO CAN BLESS YOU
WITH GOOD FORTUNE.

Who is coming to seek
my help?

How did my fawn and
I become white?

If you follow us, where
will we take you?

THE

GREEN
CHILDREN

Illustrated by IAN PENNEY

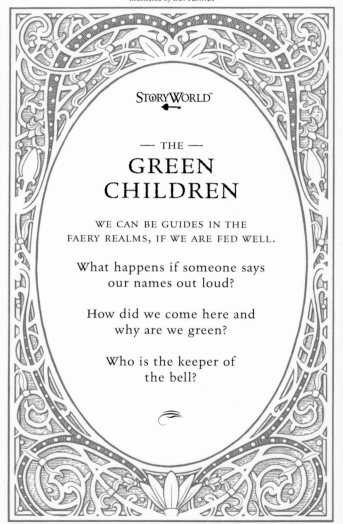

StoryWorld

— THE —

GREEN CHILDREN

WE CAN BE GUIDES IN THE
FAERY REALMS, IF WE ARE FED WELL.

What happens if someone says
our names out loud?

How did we come here and
why are we green?

Who is the keeper of
the bell?

THE
FAERY
GODMOTHER

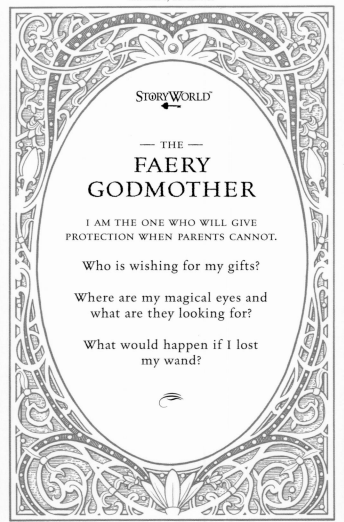

STORYWORLD™

— THE —

FAERY GODMOTHER

I AM THE ONE WHO WILL GIVE
PROTECTION WHEN PARENTS CANNOT.

Who is wishing for my gifts?

Where are my magical eyes and
what are they looking for?

What would happen if I lost
my wand?

— THE —
FAERY KING

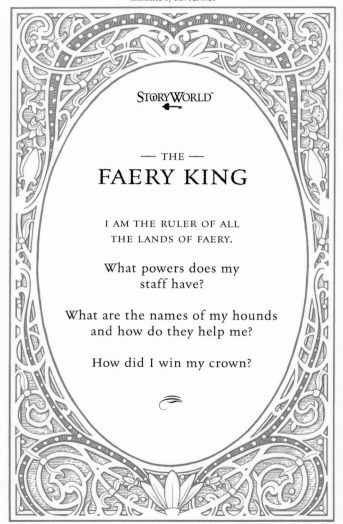

STORYWORLD

— THE —

FAERY KING

I AM THE RULER OF ALL
THE LANDS OF FAERY.

What powers does my
staff have?

What are the names of my hounds
and how do they help me?

How did I win my crown?

— THE —
SPELL OF
DANCING

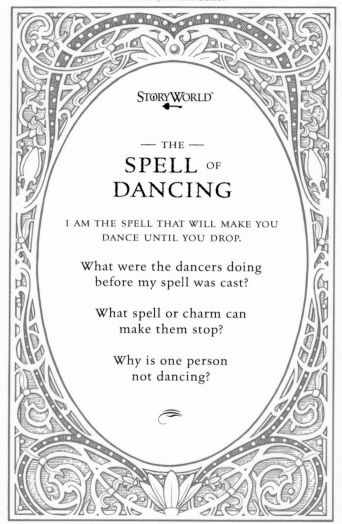

STORYWORLD™

— THE —

SPELL OF DANCING

I AM THE SPELL THAT WILL MAKE YOU
DANCE UNTIL YOU DROP.

What were the dancers doing
before my spell was cast?

What spell or charm can
make them stop?

Why is one person
not dancing?

THE
FAERY DART

Illustrated by WAYNE ANDERSON

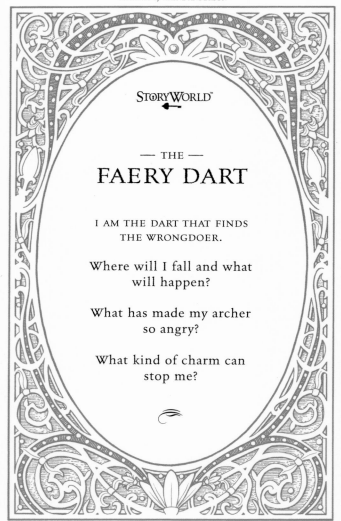

STORYWORLD™

— THE —

FAERY DART

I AM THE DART THAT FINDS
THE WRONGDOER.

Where will I fall and what
will happen?

What has made my archer
so angry?

What kind of charm can
stop me?

— THE —
FAERY CHARM

Illustrated by DEBRA MCFARLANE

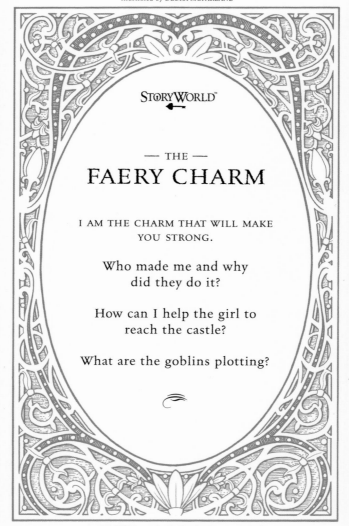

STORYWORLD™

— THE —

FAERY CHARM

I AM THE CHARM THAT WILL MAKE
YOU STRONG.

Who made me and why
did they do it?

How can I help the girl to
reach the castle?

What are the goblins plotting?

— THE —
FAERY RING

STORYWORLD™

— THE —
FAERY RING

I AM THE RING WHERE THE
FAERIES DANCE.

What happens when the faeries
dance in my circle?

Who is searching for me
and why?

When do I allow humans
to come here and dance?

THE
GUARDIAN
OF THE WAYS

Illustrated by MATILDA HARRISON

STORYWORLD™

— THE —
GUARDIAN
OF **THE WAYS**

I AM THE GUARDIAN WHO PATROLS
THE PATHS INTO FAERYLAND.

Why do I have antlers and
how do I use them?

How do I greet
unwelcome visitors?

Who just passed beneath me
and where are they going?